Social Studies Alive!®
California's Communities

TCi™

Chief Executive Officer
Bert Bower

Chief Operating Officer
Amy Larson

Director of Product Development
Maria Favata

Strategic Product Manager
Nathan Wellborne

Social Studies Team Manager
Ginger Wu

Senior Editor
Mikaila Garfinkel

Lead Editors
Lauren Kent
Alex White

Program Editors and Writers
Kate Connell
Brent Goff
Sally Isaacs
Peter Lacey
Beth Lasser
Danny Miller
Tylar Pendgraft

Production Manager
Jodi Forrest

Director of Operations
Marsha Ifurung

Senior Production Designer
Sarah Osentowski

Art Direction
Julia Foug

Production and Design Team
Jen Valenzuela
Michelle Vella

Video Developer
Dominic Mercurio

Teachers' Curriculum Institute
PO Box 1327
Rancho Cordova, CA 95741

Customer Service: 800-497-6138
www.teachtci.com

ISBN 978-1-58371-476-8
4 5 6 7 8 9 10 -SIN- 23 22 21 20

Manufactured by Sinclair Printing, Los Angeles, CA
United States of America, April 2020, Job #44621

Program Consultant

Vicki LaBoskey, Ph.D.
Professor of Education
Mills College, Oakland, California

Reading Specialist

Barbara Schubert, Ph.D.
Reading Specialist
Saint Mary's College, Moraga, California

Social Studies Content Scholars

Paul A. Barresi, J.D., Ph.D.
Professor of Political Science and
Environmental Law
*Southern New Hampshire University,
Manchester, New Hampshire*

Phillip J. VanFossen, Ph.D.
James F. Ackerman Professor of Social
Studies Education and Associate Director,
Purdue Center for Economic Education
Purdue University, West Lafayette, Indiana

Fred Walk
Lecturer, Department of Geography
Instructional Assistant Professor,
Department of History
Illinois State University, Normal, Illinois

Keith Smith, Ph.D.
Associate Professor of Political Science
University of the Pacific, Stockton, California

Wyatt Wells, Ph.D.
Professor of History
Auburn, Montgomery, Alabama

Literature Consultant

Regina M. Rees, Ph.D.
Assistant Professor
*Beeghly College of Education,
Youngstown State University,
Youngstown, Ohio*

Teacher Consultants

Judy Brodigan
Elementary Social Studies Supervisor
Lewisville Independent School District, Texas

Lynn Casey
Teacher
*Husmann Elementary School,
Crystal Lake, Illinois*

Ann Dawson
Educational Consultant and Intermediate
Curriculum Specialist
Gahanna, Ohio

Debra Elsen
Teacher
Manchester Elementary, Manchester, Maryland

Candetta Holdren
Teacher
Linlee Elementary, Lexington, Kentucky

Shirley Jacobs
Library Media Specialist
Irving Elementary School, Bloomington, Illinois

Elizabeth McKenna
Teacher
*St. Thomas Aquinas Catholic School,
Diocese of Orlando, Florida*

Mitch Pascal
Social Studies Specialist
Arlington County Schools, Arlington, Virginia

Becky Suthers
Retired Teacher
Stephen F. Austin Elementary, Weatherford, Texas

Lisa West
Instructional Specialist,
Language Arts/Social Studies
Landis Elementary School, Houston, Texas

Tiffany Wilson
Teacher
Corbell Elementary, Frisco, Texas

Beth Yankee
Teacher
*The Woodward School for Technology and Research,
Kalamazoo, Michigan*

Contents

A friend or family member is coming to your school.
Can you tell the person how to find your classroom?

1. Write down how to get from your school's main entrance to
    your classroom.

    _____

    _____

    _____

    _____

2. Draw a picture in the box that shows the route to your classroom.
    Label places like "hallway" and "office."

1. Our Community Is on Planet Earth

Label the hemispheres that are shaded dark gray. Label the equator and the prime meridian. Be sure to spell the names correctly.

2. Our Community Is on a Continent

Label the five oceans and the seven continents on the map.
Be sure to spell the names correctly.

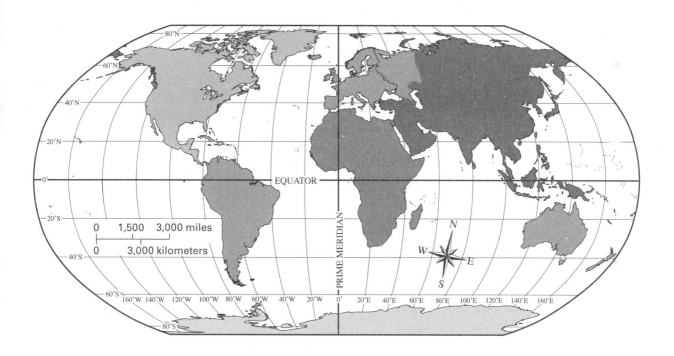

3. Our Community Is in a Country

Label five countries on the map. Be sure to spell the names correctly.

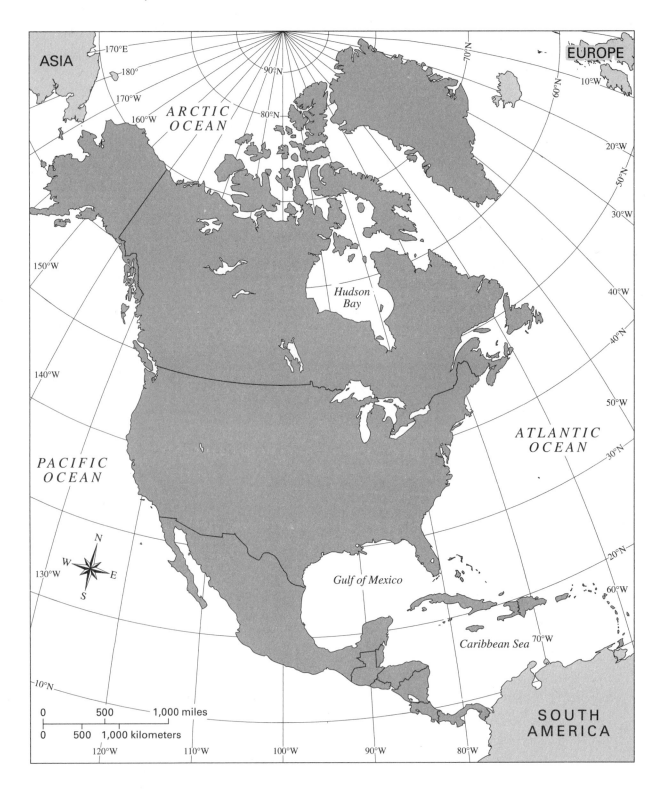

4. Our Community Is in a State

Label the six states on the map that are shaded gray. Be sure to spell the names correctly.

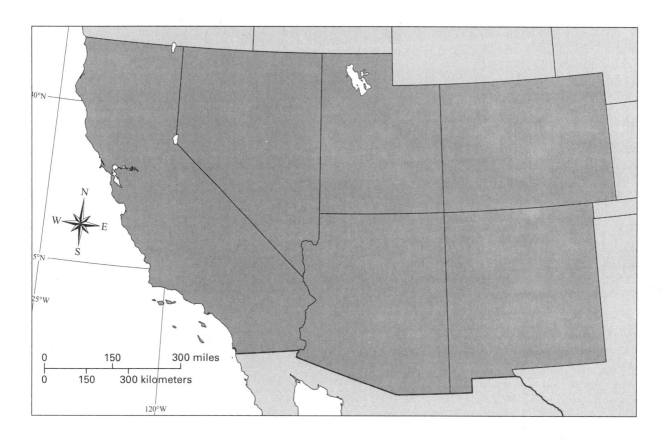

5. Finding Communities in a State

Label the four cities on the map. Be sure to spell
the names correctly.

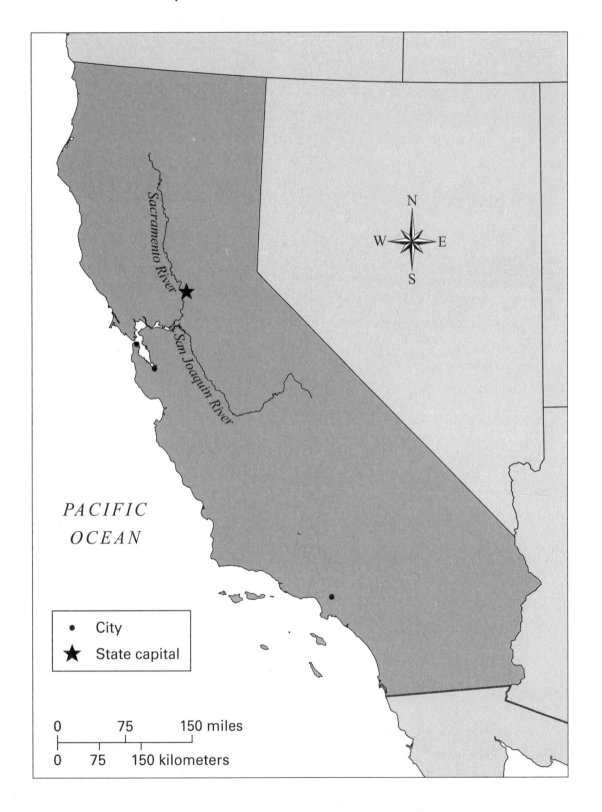

Where in the World Is Our Community?

Step 1: Write a letter that invites someone special to visit your community.

- Write the person's name in the greeting.
- Fill in the blanks to tell your guest where in the world you are.
- Write the name of your community. Describe two interesting places there.
- Sign your letter.

Dear _____ ,

    Please visit my community! Here's how to find me. Look on planet _____ . Find the _____ Hemisphere. Then find my continent, _____ . Next find my country, _____ . Finally, find my state, _____ , and my community, _____ .

    There are two places here that you must visit. First, you should visit _____ because _____ _____ . You should also visit _____ because _____ _____ .

                Your friend,

                _____

Step 2: Draw a map of a place in your community. The place should have both natural features (such as lakes, mountains, and trees) and features made by people (such as buildings and roads). In your map, include

- a title.
- symbols or colors, such as dotted lines for crosswalks, green for parks, blue for water.

Picture yourself as one of the explorers you have read about.
Write a diary page about one day of your trip to North America.
Who or what do you see on this day? What happens to you?

In your writing, be sure to:

- introduce the narrator and/or characters.
- organize an event sequence that unfolds naturally.
- use dialogue and descriptions to develop experiences or show character responses.
- use words and phrases to signal event order.
- provide a sense of closure to your letter.

Find your community in your state.

- Draw an outline of California in the space below. Include the Pacific Ocean and states that border California.
- Find out where your community is located.
- Draw a dot to show where your community is.

Write the name of your community here:

Complete this map of your classroom.
Follow your teacher's directions.

On the map, you will draw directions on the compass rose. You
will also draw objects in your classroom, show which direction
things are from each other, and how far they are from each other.

Read Section 1, The 50 States, and Section 2, Mapping California. Then follow these directions.

- Label the compass rose.
- Label the map key.
- Label the scale.
- Find your state on the map, and outline it.
- Find your community in your state. Draw a dot for your community.

Read Section 3, The State Capitol. Where is the State Capitol?

- Add and label a dot on the map with the name of your community.
- Label the dot on the map with the name of the place you just read about.
- Draw a line from your community to that dot. Use your ruler to measure the distance between them. Write the distance on the line.

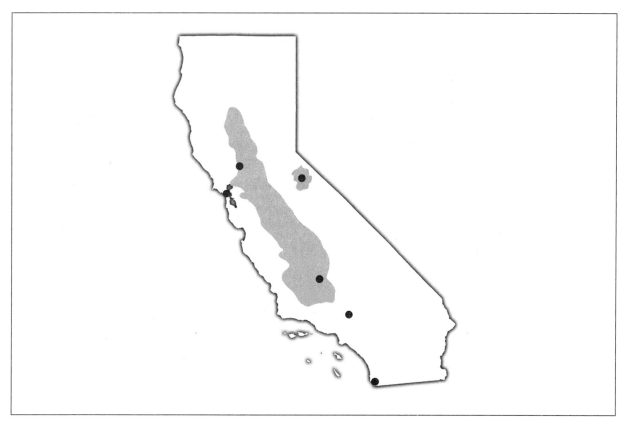

Complete the sentences below.

The distance from _____
                                    (name of my community)

to the state capitol building is about _____ miles.

The direction from _____
                                    (name of my community)

to the state capitol building is _____ .

Read Section 4, The Golden Gate Bridge. Where is the Golden Gate Bridge?

- Add and label a dot on the map with the name of your community.
- Label the dot on the map with the name of the place you just read about.
- Draw a line from your community to that dot. Use your ruler to measure the distance between them. Write the distance on the line.

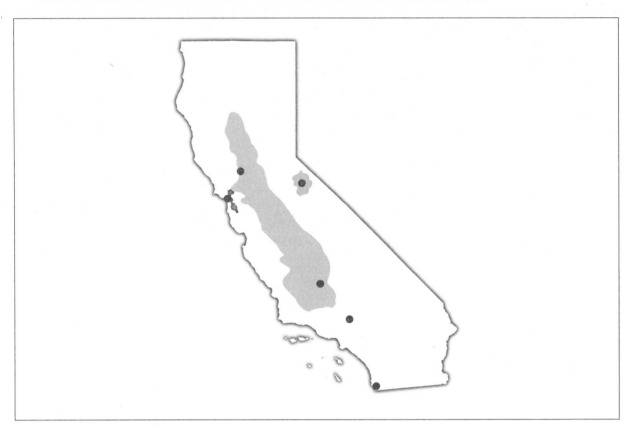

Complete the sentences below.

The distance from _____

(name of my community)

to the Golden Gate Bridge is about _____ miles.

The direction from _____

(name of my community)

to the Golden Gate Bridge is _____ .

Read Section 5, Yosemite National Park. Where is Yosemite National Park?

- Add and label a dot on the map with the name of your community.
- Label the dot on the map with the name of the place you just read about.
- Draw a line from your community to that dot. Use your ruler to measure the distance between them. Write the distance on the line.

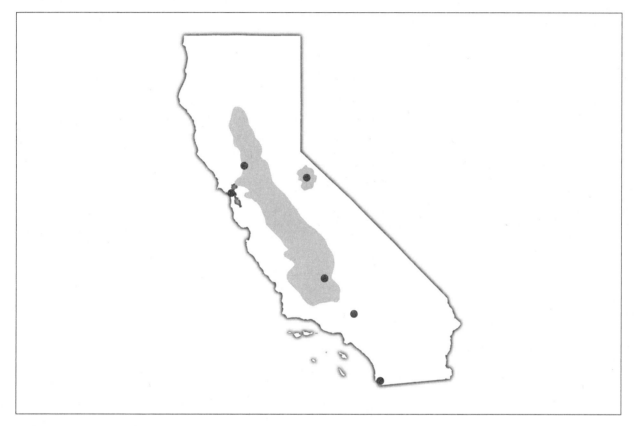

Complete the sentences below.

The distance from _____
(name of my community)

to Yosemite National Park is about _____ miles.

The direction from _____
(name of my community)

to Yosemite National Park is _____ .

Read Section 6, Central Valley Farms. Where is the Central Valley?

- Add and label a dot on the map with the name of your community.
- Label the dot on the map with the name of the place you just read about. Draw a line from your community to that dot. Use your ruler to measure the distance between them. Write the distance on the line.

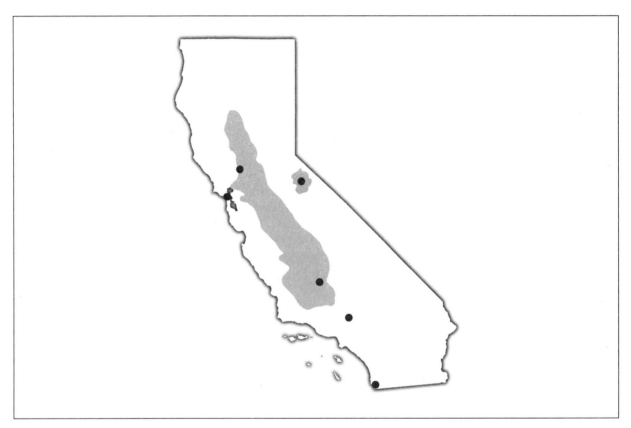

Complete the sentences below.

The distance from _____
(name of my community)

to the Central Valley is about _____ miles.

The direction from _____
(name of my community)

to the Central Valley is _____ .

Read Section 7, Olvera Street. Where is Olvera Street?

- Add and label a dot on the map with the name of your community.
- Label the dot on the map with the name of the place you just read about.
- Draw a line from your community to that dot. Use your ruler to measure the distance between them. Write the distance on the line.

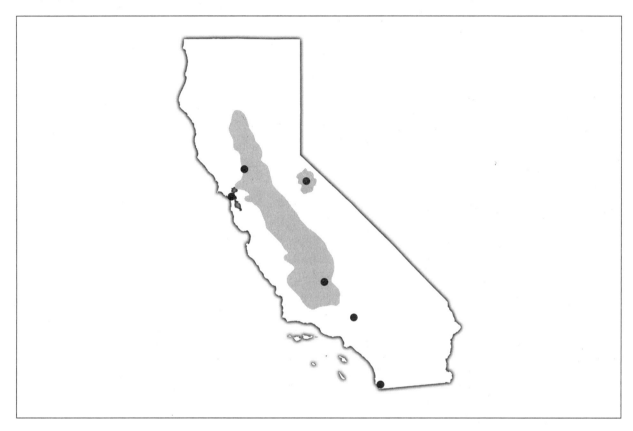

Complete the sentences below.

The distance from _____

(name of my community)

to Olvera Street is about _____ miles.

The direction from _____

(name of my community)

to Olvera Street is _____ .

Read Section 8, The San Diego Zoo. Where is the San Diego Zoo?

- Add and label a dot on the map with the name of your community.
- Label the dot on the map with the name of the place and its state.
- Draw a line from your community to that dot. Use your ruler to measure the distance between them. Write the distance on the line.

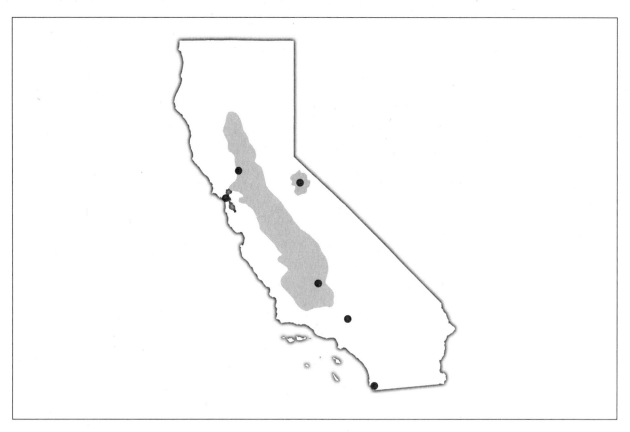

Complete the sentences below.

The distance from _____
(name of my community)

to the San Diego Zoo is about _____ miles.

The direction from _____
(name of my community)

to the San Diego Zoo is _____ .

What Special Places Tell Our Community's Story?

Step 1: Find a statue, building, or other place that helps tell the story of your community. Draw it on this postcard. Write its name in one corner.

Step 2: Use the back of the postcard to tell a friend why the special place is important in your community. Address your postcard.

Step 3: Now draw directions from your community to the special place you wrote about. Be sure to label your map and use the compass rose to write the directions.

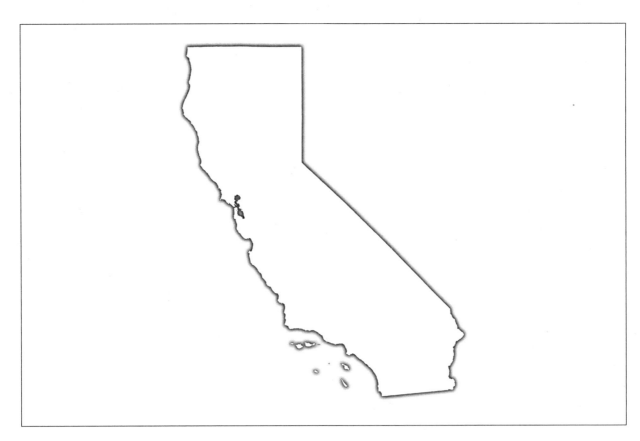

Teresa lives in another country. She has heard that the Fourth of July is special in the United States, but she doesn't know why. She wants to know more about it. Tell her about this day by filling in the blanks in the letter below.

_____

(date)

Dear Teresa,

On the Fourth of July, Americans celebrate

_____ .

People like to show American flags on this day.

That's because the flag stands for _____

_____ .

We also have other Fourth of July traditions,

like _____

and _____ .

As you can see, it's a big day for us!

Your pal,

_____

Think of a tradition that you like. It can be anything that people do together year after year. On the lines below, tell what the tradition is.

_____

_____

Draw a picture of this tradition in the box.

Look at the list of places below. Select one you would like to visit. Use books and other sources in the classroom, in a library, or at home to find out where this place is in California.

- Santa Cruz Boardwalk

- Hollywood Walk of Fame

- the Transamerica Pyramid

- Lake Tahoe

- Disneyland

Now follow these directions:

1. Write the name of the place you chose next to its dot on the map.

2. On the map, draw a straight line from your community to this place.

3. Use your map ruler to measure the distance between the two dots. Write the distance on the line.

4. Draw an arrow on the compass rose to show which direction to travel from your community to the new place.

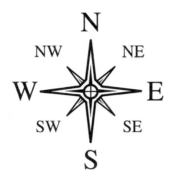

Write the name of your community on the line in the box below. Then draw a picture to show what the geography of your community is like. Are there hills and mountains nearby? A river, a lake, or an ocean? What is the weather like? What kinds of trees or plants grow where you live?

Read Section 1, What Is Geography?, and Section 2, Adapting to Geography. Fill in this table as you read.

- Write a definition for each term in your own words.
- Draw a symbol to illustrate each term.

Term	Definition	Symbol
physical feature		
physical geography		
climate		
natural resources		
natural hazard		
adapt		
pollution		
conservation		

Read Sections 3 through 6. Fill in this table as you read.

Name and Location of Community	Physical Features (examples: river, mountain)	Climate (examples: temperature, rainfall)	Natural Resources (examples: wood, fish)
Truckee			
San Diego			
Davis			
Palm Springs			

How Do Natural Features and Resources Affect Our Community?

Step 1: Write a paragraph that identifies and describes a major landform in your community.

Step 2: What kinds of natural resources does that major landform provide? List them below.

Step 3: What other natural resources are found in your community? What goods and services do these natural resources provide? Write your answers in the chart below.

Natural Resource	How We Use It

Step 4: What natural threats or challenges are found in your community? How do people meet them? Write your answers in the chart below.

Natural Threat	How We Deal With It

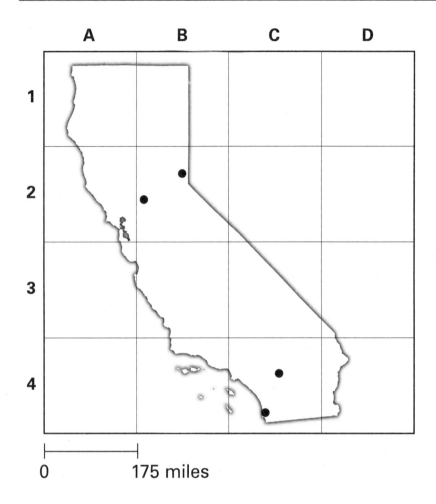

1. Use your ruler to measure the map scale.
   How many miles is one inch on the scale? _____

2. Use your ruler to measure the side of
   one of the squares on the grid. How
   long is the side of one square in miles? _____

3. The dots stand for the locations you've read about.
   Write the location names next to the correct dots.

4. Draw a dot where your community is. Write the
   name of your community next to the dot.

5. What square of the map grid is your community in? _____

6. What square of the map grid is Truckee in? _____

7. What square of the map grid is San Diego in? _____

8. What square of the map grid is Davis in? _____

9. What square of the map grid is Palm Springs in? _____

10. Use your ruler to measure the distance between Truckee and San Diego. About how many miles is this? _____

11. About how many miles is it from Truckee to Davis? _____

12. Which location is farthest from your community—Truckee, San Diego, Davis, or Palm Springs? _____

13. About how many miles is it from your community to that location? _____

You will draw how you and your family have adapted to your community's geography. Choose two of these for your community: physical features, climate, and natural resources.

- Show how you and your family have adapted to these two parts of geography. Draw a picture in the box below.
- For each part of geography you chose, write a sentence to describe how you adapted.

Think about the geography and climate where you live and how they affect you.

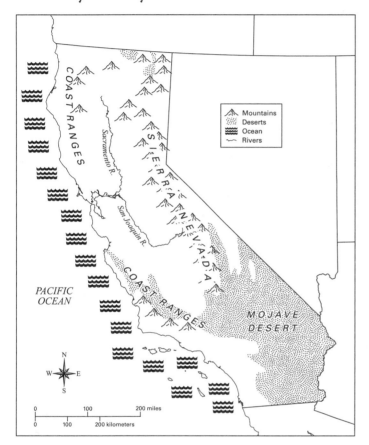

How does the environment affect your life? For example, how does it affect the clothes you wear or the activities you do?

Imagine you lived in another part of California. If you lived there, how do you think the environment would affect your life? How would your life be different?

Read Sections 1–3. On this map, mark where the Hupa, the Chumash, and the Miwok lived. Use a different color for each group. In the key, color the boxes to match.

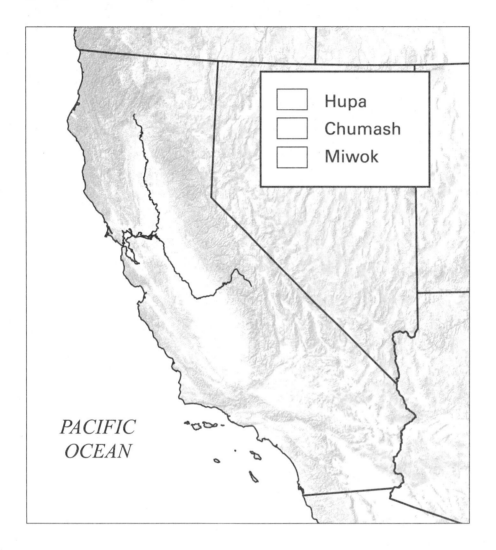

Hupa
Chumash
Miwok

PACIFIC
OCEAN

In the table below, list the natural resources each group used for each purpose. In the "Other items" row, also include the purpose of each resource. An example has been done for you.

	Hupa	Chumash	Miwok
Food			
Shelter			
Religion			
Other items	roots and stems to make baskets		

How did the natural environment affect the resources each group had?

The Hupa

The Chumash

The Miwok

Read Section 4, California Indians and Settlers. In the speech balloon for each person below, complete the sentence from that person's point of view.

I came to California to . . .

Spanish Settler

After the Spanish arrived, my life changed because . . .

California Indian

How did the arrival of more settlers in 1848 affect Indians' lives?

How Did American Indians Live in Our Community?

American Indians used natural resources they found to meet their needs. Because each group's resources varied, they had different ways of life. Use the library or Internet, or visit a local historical society, to learn how American Indians in your community lived long ago. List the resources that you used for research, such as Web sites, maps, and books.

Step 1: Find the name of an American Indian group that lived in your community. What is the name of that community?

Step 2: Draw a picture showing a small village belonging to that group. Include one or more people working or eating next to a home.

Label the clothing, home, food, and tools with the name of any natural resources used to make them. Your labels may include resources such as feathers, wood, deerskin, trees, grasses, or clay.

Describe the village's location. Explain why it was built there.

Step 3: People show what they believe through their religion, stories, songs, tales, and traditions. Continue your research and learn about the culture of an American Indian group that used to live or now lives in your community.

In the first two boxes, write about the group's religious beliefs and customs.

In the last box, write about one animal or person featured in the songs, poems, or stories of this group.

Religious beliefs
Traditions and customs
Stories, songs, or other folklore

Where I found this information:

Part 1: If you wanted to learn about the life and culture of an American Indian group that lived in your community, what questions would you ask? Write five questions you would ask to learn more about this group.

Part 2: Choose one of the questions you wrote, and write a one-paragraph answer to it. Use multiple resources to help you answer the question.

Where I found this information:

Compare each of the groups you studied. For each pair of groups, write two sentences:
- one that tells how the groups were similar
- one that tells how the groups differed

Hupa and Chumash

Similarity:

Difference:

Hupa and Miwok

Similarity:

Difference:

Miwok and Chumash

Similarity:

Difference:

Draw a picture in the box below that shows you in a new place.

Were you happy? Sad? A little scared? Angry? Show how you felt. Look at the faces below to help you. Then finish the sentences at the bottom of the page.

When I _____ ,

I felt _____ because _____ .

1. Explorers and Missions

Draw a way in which European explorers or Spanish missionaries changed California.

Describe the experience of American Indians in the mission system.

2. Why Settlers Came to California

Draw a scene that describes what drove people to California in 1848.

What brought immigrants to California in the 1920s and 1930s?

3. How Settlers Traveled to California

Draw a method of transportation that people used to get to California.

Why was traveling to California difficult in the past?

4. Settlers from Around the World

Where do immigrants to California come from?

What contributions have they brought to California?

5. Life for Immigrants

What challenges do immigrants face in California?

What opportunities do immigrants have in California?

6. Becoming a U.S. Citizen

What are the benefits of being a U.S. citizen?

How can a person become a U.S. citizen?

How Has Our Community Changed Over Time?

Step 1: Using primary sources (such as photographs, oral histories, letters, and newspapers) and secondary sources (such as textbooks and journal articles), research how different generations interacted within our community. A generation is a group of people born and living during the same time. Compare how people's lives were affected by each topic a century (one hundred years) ago, a decade (ten years) ago, and in the present.

Topics	A Century Ago	A Decade Ago	The Present
Kinds of Transportation			
Ways of Providing Water			
Sources of Power			
Types of Work			
Kinds of Clothing			
Types of Recreation			

Step 2: How did geography affect how each generation interacted within our community? Use evidence from multiple visual or print sources to support your ideas.

Step 3: Write a paragraph that describes how decisions made today will affect these topics for future generations.

Draw a picture in the box below. Show how you would help
an immigrant to the United States feel more at home.

Write a narrative, or story, to explain what you would do first,
second, and third to help an immigrant.

_____

_____

_____

_____

_____

Find an older student or adult who came to your community from another country. Interview that person.

Step 1: Ask these questions, and write the person's answers.

What country did you come from? _____

Why did you leave your country? _____

_____

How did you feel when you left your country? _____

_____

How is your life here different from your life before? _____

_____

_____

In what ways is life here the same as it was in your first

country? _____

_____

Why did you choose our community? _____

_____

Ask some more questions of your own. Write the questions and the person's answers on a separate sheet of paper.

Step 2: The following items can help you learn about the person. Ask if the person can show you any of these:
- papers, such as a visa or passport
- letters, maybe from relatives still at home
- photographs showing homes, villages, or cities in the old country

Step 3: Use everything you have learned to write a narrative, or story, about the person you interviewed. Begin by writing the person's name in the title. Tell about the person in your own words.

In your writing, be sure to:

- tell about the events in this person's life in the order they happened.
- include what the person thought and felt.
- use words that help show the order of events such as *then* or *next*.
- write a closing sentence that restates your main idea.

Meet a New Member of Our Community:

_____

Listen carefully to the story about Rosa Parks. Think of words that could go on a plaque for the Rosa Parks monument. Write them in the spaces below.

Rosa Parks

What did she do to improve her community? _____

_____

_____

_____

When did she do this? _____

How have her actions helped people in other communities?

_____

_____

_____

1. Good Citizens Help Their Community

Complete the web to tell ways you can be a good citizen.
One example has been done for you.

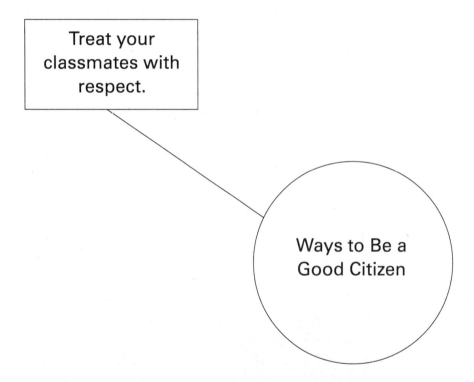

Treat your classmates with respect.

Ways to Be a Good Citizen

2. Clara Barton Helps Soldiers

Think of words that could go on a plaque for a monument to Clara Barton. Write them in the spaces below.

Clara Barton

What did she do to improve her community? _____

_____

_____

_____

When did she do this? _____

How have her actions helped people in other communities?

_____

_____

_____

3. César Chávez Helps Farmworkers

Think of words that could go on a plaque for a monument to César Chávez. Write them in the spaces below.

César Chávez

What did he do to improve his community? _____

_____

_____

_____

When did he do this? _____

How have his actions helped people in other communities?

_____

_____

_____

4. Ruby Bridges Helps African Americans

Think of words that could go on a plaque for
a monument to Ruby Bridges. Write them in
the spaces below.

Ruby Bridges

What did she do to improve her community? _____

_____

_____

_____

When did she do this? _____

How have her actions helped people in other communities?

_____

_____

_____

5. Doniece Sandoval Helps the Homeless

Think of words that could go on a plaque for a monument to Doniece Sandoval. Write them in the spaces below.

Doniece Sandoval

What did she do to improve her community? _____

_____

_____

_____

When did she do this? _____

How have her actions helped people in other communities?

_____

_____

_____

6. Judy Heumann Helps Disabled People

Think of words that could go on a plaque for
a monument to Judy Heumann. Write them
in the spaces below.

Judy Heumann

What did she do to improve her community? _____

_____

_____

_____

When did she do this? _____

How have her actions helped people in other communities?

_____

_____

_____

How Have People in Our Community Used the Land Over Time?

Step 1: Research how people have changed your community's geography over time. You can look at primary sources, such as old maps and photographs. Use the Internet or the library to find important events that changed your community for each topic.

Event Related To	Year(s)	What Happened
Soil		
Water		
Mineral resources		
Location of community		
Physical features		
Buildings		
Schools and colleges		
Recreation (parks, pools, paths)		
Streets		

Step 2: Put the events in your chart on the timeline to show how your community changed over time.

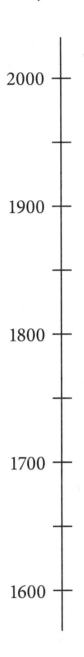

Where I found this information:

Create a timeline showing how the community of Berkeley changed over time.

Who are the heroes in your community? Research someone who has made your community better. Draw a monument for this hero. Your award should include:

- the hero's name.
- a drawing that shows how this person improved the community.
- a description of what this person did.

Write the name of your assigned person or department on the line.

Brainstorm ideas about the tasks your person or department might do. Write one or two tasks inside the outline of City Hall.

Person or Department: _____

1. The Mayor and the City Council

You chose this office as the one to respond to a letter. Tell the person who wrote the letter why your office can help. Complete the reply below.

_____

Dear _____,

    I work in the office of

_____.

We can help you with the problem

you wrote about because this

office is responsible for _____

_____.

This office is also responsible

for _____

_____.

       Your public servant,

    _____

2. The City Manager

You chose this office as the one to respond to a letter. Tell the person who wrote the letter why your office can help. Complete the reply below.

Dear _____,

    I work in the office of

_____.

We can help you with the problem

you wrote about because this

office is responsible for _____

_____.

This office is also responsible

for _____

_____.

          Your public servant,

          _____

3. The City Clerk

You chose this office as the one to respond to a letter. Tell the person who wrote the letter why your office can help. Complete the reply below.

Dear _____,

    I work in the office of

_____.

We can help you with the problem

you wrote about because this

office is responsible for _____

_____.

This office is also responsible

for _____

_____.

          Your public servant,

          _____

4. The Parks and Recreation Department

You chose this office as the one to respond to a letter. Tell the person who wrote the letter why your office can help. Complete the reply below.

Dear _____,

    I work in the office of

_____.

We can help you with the problem

you wrote about because this

office is responsible for _____

_____.

This office is also responsible

for _____

_____.

        Your public servant,

_____

5. The Public Library

You chose this office as the one to respond to a letter. Tell the person who wrote the letter why your office can help. Complete the reply below.

Public
Library

Dear _____,

    I work in the office of

_____.

We can help you with the problem

you wrote about because this

office is responsible for _____

_____.

This office is also responsible

for _____

_____.

        Your public servant,

        _____

6. The Fire Department

You chose this office as the one to respond to a letter. Tell the person who wrote the letter why your office can help. Complete the reply below.

```
                    _____

Dear _____,

        I work in the office of

_____.

We can help you with the problem

you wrote about because this

office is responsible for _____

_____.

This office is also responsible

for _____

_____.

                Your public servant,

                    _____
```

7. The Police Department

You chose this office as the one to respond to a letter. Tell the person who wrote the letter why your office can help. Complete the reply below.

Dear _____,

     I work in the office of

_____.

We can help you with the problem

you wrote about because this

office is responsible for _____

_____.

This office is also responsible

for _____

_____.

       Your public servant,

_____

8. The Planning Department

You chose this office as the one to respond to a letter. Tell the person who wrote the letter why your office can help. Complete the reply below.

Dear _____,

    I work in the office of

_____.

We can help you with the problem

you wrote about because this

office is responsible for _____

_____.

This office is also responsible

for _____

_____.

           Your public servant,

_____

9. The Public Works Department

You chose this office as the one to respond to a letter. Tell the person who wrote the letter why your office can help. Complete the reply below.

_____

Dear _____,

    I work in the office of

_____.

We can help you with the problem

you wrote about because this

office is responsible for _____

_____.

This office is also responsible

for _____

_____.

        Your public servant,

_____

Read Section 10, California's Government, and Section 11, The U.S. Government. Find two or three things about these governments that are the same. Write them where the circles overlap. An example has been done for you.

What is different about these governments? Write two or three things that are different in each of the other two parts of the diagram. Some examples have been done for you.

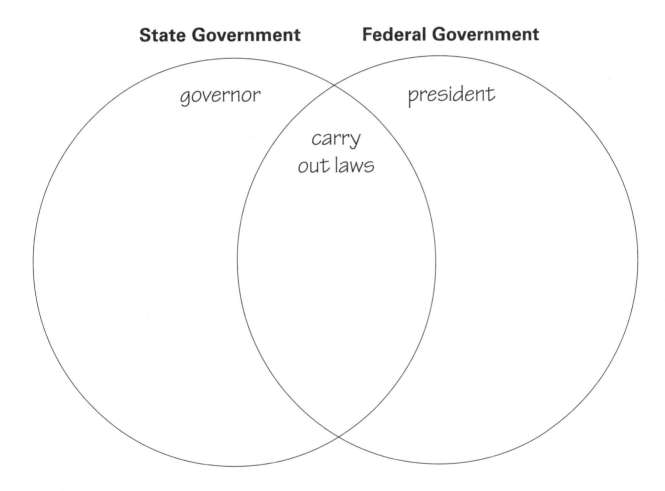

State Government   **Federal Government**

governor

carry
out laws

president

What can happen if someone breaks a state or federal law?

12. Tribal Governments

What does a tribal government provide for an American Indian community?

What similarities does a tribal government have to California's governments?

What differences does a tribal government have to California's governments?

When do tribal governments and California's governments work together?

How Is American Indian Government Like Our Government?

Step 1: Use the library, the Internet, or other sources of community information to learn more about your local government. Write the name of your community in the space provided. Use the information you research to answer the following questions.

The Government of _____

1. What is the leader of your community called? _____

_____

2. How is the leader chosen? _____

_____

3. What jobs does the leader do? _____

_____

4. Does the leader make all the decisions? If not, who does? _____

_____

5. How do the leaders help to improve the community or solve problems?

_____

_____

_____

Step 2: Find the nearest American Indian community to where you live. Write the name of the tribe in the space provided. Answer the following questions about their government.

The Government of _____

1. What is the leader of the tribal government called? _____

_____

2. How is the leader chosen? _____

_____

3. What jobs does the leader do? _____

_____

4. Does the leader make all the decisions? If not, who does? _____

_____

5. How do the leaders help to improve the community or solve problems?

_____

_____

_____

Step 3: Use the information you have researched to answer the question: How is American Indian government like our local government?

Read the story below. Discuss the blank lines with your partner. Decide what words should go on the lines. Use the Word Bank to help you. Then write the words on the lines. Some words may be used more than once.

<table>
<tr><td colspan="2">Word Bank</td></tr>
<tr><td>Constitution</td><td>mayor</td></tr>
<tr><td>federal</td><td>president</td></tr>
<tr><td>governor</td><td>state</td></tr>
<tr><td>local</td><td></td></tr>
</table>

There was trouble in Little Rock. People were angry that black students were going to enter Central High School. The _____ of Arkansas warned that "blood will run in the streets."

The governor was the head of the _____ government. He sent soldiers to keep the black students out of Central High.

The governor's action went against the U.S. Supreme Court. The Supreme Court is part of the _____ government.

The Supreme Court's job is to say what the laws mean. The Court

had said that keeping black and white students apart was against the

_____.

A judge told the governor to take the soldiers away. People were still

angry. The mayor of Little Rock was afraid that someone might get hurt. He

asked for help from the _____ of the United States.

The president is part of the _____government.

President Eisenhower sent U.S. Army troops to keep order in Little

Rock. Usually, keeping the peace is the job of the _____

government. But Eisenhower had a reason to act. He was protecting the

students' rights under the _____.

What are three levels of government where you live?
Fill in the information for each level of government.

- Write the name of your country, state, and community.
- Research services that each level of government provides for you. You can find information from the library, books, government Web sites, or magazines.
- List two services each level of government provides. List your sources.

Federal Government

Country: _____

Services: _____

_____

Sources: _____

State Government

State: _____

Services: _____

_____

Sources: _____

Local Government

Community: _____

Services: _____

_____

Sources: _____

1. Think of a time when you had no voice in a decision that affected you. Then answer the questions below.

   What was the decision?

   _____

   Did you agree with the decision? _____

   How did you feel about not having a voice in this decision? Draw a face in the box to show your feelings.

2. Think of a time when you did have a voice in a decision that affected you. Then answer the questions below.

   What was the decision?

   _____

   Did you agree with the decision? _____

   How did you feel about having a voice in this decision? Draw a face in the box to show your feelings.

3. How important is it to you to have a voice in decisions that affect you? Circle one. Then support your opinion with reasons.

   Not important   **Important**   **Very important**

1. People Choose Our Leaders

How are leaders selected in a republic?

Draw and label one responsibility of government leaders.

Draw and label one responsibility of citizens.

2. Going to Public Meetings

Complete this sentence:

Going to a public meeting gives people a voice in their

community because _____

_____.

Draw yourself in the picture. Then write what you would
say at a public meeting.

We should build a _____ in the park

because _____

_____.

3. Taking Part in Peaceful Demonstrations

Complete this sentence:

Taking part in a peaceful demonstration gives people a

voice in their community because _____

_____.

Draw your group in the picture. In the speech bubble, write
what you would chant at a peaceful demonstration. Write
messages on the signs.

© Teachers' Curriculum Institute

4. Supporting a Candidate

Complete this sentence:

Supporting a candidate gives people a voice in their

community because _____

_____ .

Draw yourself in the picture. Then write which candidate
you would support and why.

I would support candidate _____

because _____

_____ .

5. Voting

Complete this sentence:

Voting gives people a voice in their community because

_____.

Draw yourself in the picture. Then write how you voted
and why.

I voted to build a _____ in the

park because _____

_____.

How Can We Take a Stand in Our Community?

Step 1: Think about a place in your neighborhood or community that could be changed for the better. There might be some open land, an empty lot, or a big store that has gone out of business. Decide on a better way to use this space. Your idea should show your understanding of what people in your community need and want.

Step 2: Draw a picture showing how the space might be used.

Step 3: Write an opinion statement. First, name the place, such as "The old paper mill on State Road." Then, tell your idea for its use.

_____ should be turned into

_____

_____ .

Step 4: Use the opinion statement you just wrote as the topic sentence for a paragraph that explains the reasons for your opinion. Use linking words like *then, also, but,* or *and.* Be sure your writing follows this pattern:

- Opinion statement
- Reason 1 for your opinion
- Explanation and support for reason 1
- Reason 2 for your opinion
- Explanation and support for reason 2
- Concluding sentence

Your community wants to have a Benjamin Franklin
Day. Help write a proclamation to announce this
special day. Think of reasons to honor Franklin.
Then finish the "Whereas" statements.

PROCLAMATION: BENJAMIN FRANKLIN DAY

Whereas Benjamin Franklin, an American of great

public virtue, was born on January 17, 1706, and

Whereas _____

_____ , and

Whereas _____

_____ , and

Whereas _____

_____ ,

Therefore, January 17 shall be known as Benjamin

Franklin Day in our community.

Think about an issue in your community or school. In the space below, create a poster. Show how you feel about the issue. Include two or three drawings. Also include a short slogan that is easy to remember.

Look at this picture of Earth. Add to the picture by drawing
or writing some of the things that make up the environment.

1. Air Pollution

Create the first half of an Environmental Solution cartoon.
Follow the steps below.

1. Draw the air pollution problem that Los Angeles faces.

2. Fill in the speech bubble for each character. Have the characters explain the problem they want to solve.

Problem

© Teachers' Curriculum Institute

2. Tree Musketeers to the Rescue

Create the second half of an Environmental Solution cartoon.

1. Draw one way the Tree Musketeers helped to solve the problem. Include the two characters from the first half of your cartoon.

2. Create a speech bubble for each character. Have the characters tell how they helped to solve the problem.

Solution

3. A Huge Oil Spill

Create the first half of an Environmental Solution cartoon.

1. Draw the problem that occurred at the Union Oil drilling platform.

2. Fill in the speech bubble for each character. Have the characters explain the problem they want to solve.

Problem

4. Stopping Oil Spills

Create the second half of an Environmental Solution cartoon.

1. Draw one way the government or the communities helped to solve the problem. Include the two characters from the first half of your cartoon.

2. Create a speech bubble for each character. Have the characters tell how the government or the communities helped to solve the problem.

Solution

5. Natural Gas Leaks

Create the first half of an Environmental Solution cartoon.

1. Draw the problem that occurred at the gas storage facility in Aliso Canyon

2. Fill in the speech bubble for each character. Have the characters explain the problem they want to solve.

Problem

6. Making Sure Communities Are Safe

Create the second half of an Environmental Solution cartoon.

1. Draw one way the community helped to solve the problem. Include the two characters from the first half of your cartoon.

2. Create a speech bubble for each character. Have the characters tell how the community helped to solve the problem.

Solution

Does Our Community Protect the Environment?

Step 1: Find out about an individual or group in your community that does one of these jobs:

- fights pollution
- saves energy or water
- protects habitats
- recycles or reduces waste
- keeps animals safe
- plants trees or protects soil

Step 2: Complete the organizer below. Try to find both primary and secondary sources about the individual or group. A primary source might be an individual's website. A secondary source might be an article about an event a group staged in the past. Write down where you found your sources.

Who	
What	
Where	
When	
Why	
How	

Step 3: Create a poster showing how this individual or group helps protect the environment.

Step 4: List two natural features or landforms in your community that you want to be protected. Then write what actions you can take to protect it.

What things in your life use energy? Where might that energy come from?
Answer these questions by completing the diagram below.

1. In the big circle, draw at least four things in your
    life that use energy.

2. On the left side of the diagram, write one
    nonrenewable source of energy in each circle.
    On the right side of the diagram, write one
    renewable source of energy in each circle.
    Use the Word Bank to help you.

> **Word Bank**
> water
> natural gas
> oil
> wind
> coal
> sunlight

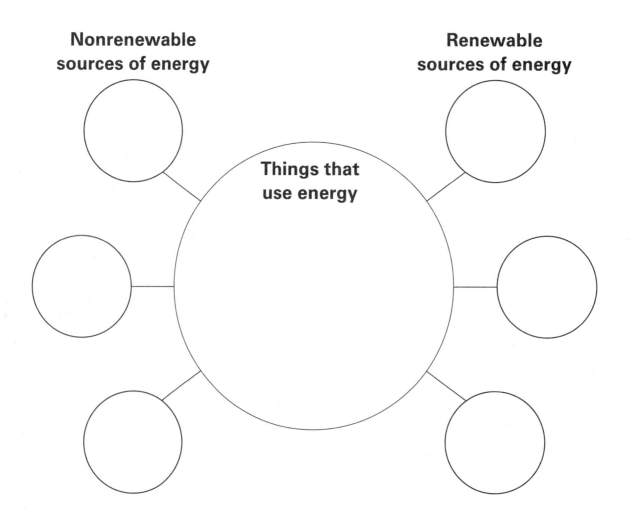

**Nonrenewable
sources of energy**

**Renewable
sources of energy**

**Things that
use energy**

3. Using nonrenewable sources of energy can
    cause problems for the environment. What
    are two of these problems?

    _____

    _____

    _____

    _____

4. Getting more energy from renewable sources is
    challenging. What are two reasons for this?

    _____

    _____

    _____

    _____

5. Suppose the world got most of its energy from
    renewable sources. How might the environment
    be different? Write one way below.

    _____

    _____

    _____

Create the first half of an Environmental Solution
cartoon for your community.

1. Draw a picture of an environmental problem in your
    community. Include at least two characters. (You can
    be one of them.)

2. Create a speech bubble for each character. Have the
    characters explain the problem.

Problem

Create the second half of your Environmental Solution cartoon.

1. Think about how your community might solve the problem. Draw a picture of your idea. Include the characters from the first half of your cartoon.

2. Create a speech bubble for each character. Have the characters tell how the problem is being solved.

Solution

Design a bumper sticker about a problem or issue. Choose a topic that you feel strongly about. Include three to five words on your bumper sticker. If you like, you can also include a simple picture or symbol.

Draw your bumper sticker anywhere on the car below.

Read Sections 1-3 in the Student Text with your group. Find three ideas for ways to help protect the environment. For each idea, complete the sentence on one of the cars. Then draw a bumper sticker for that idea anywhere on the car.

One way to help protect the environment is

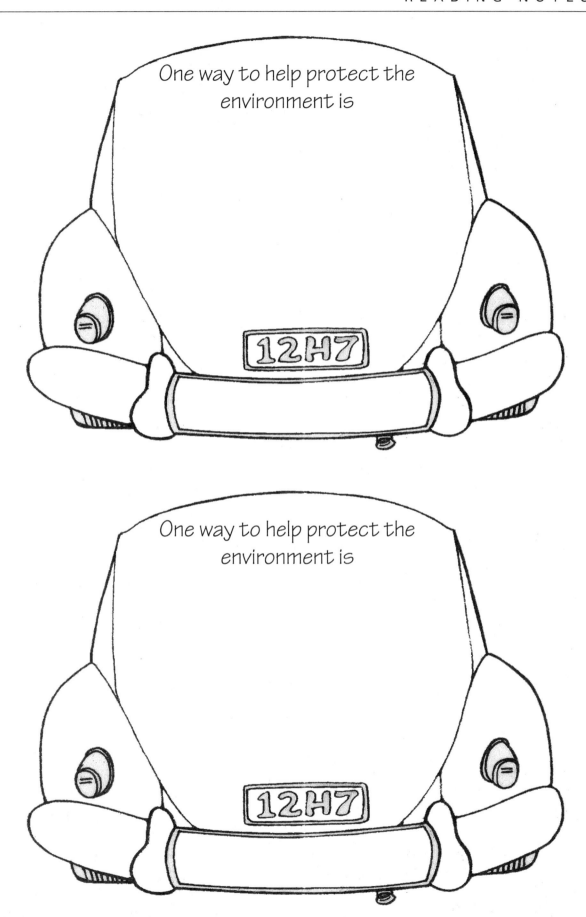

One way to help protect the
environment is

12H7

One way to help protect the
environment is

12H7

Read Sections 4-5 in the Student Text with your group. Find three ideas for ways to help wildlife. For each idea, complete the sentence on one of the cars. Then draw a bumper sticker for that idea anywhere on the car.

One way to help wildlife is

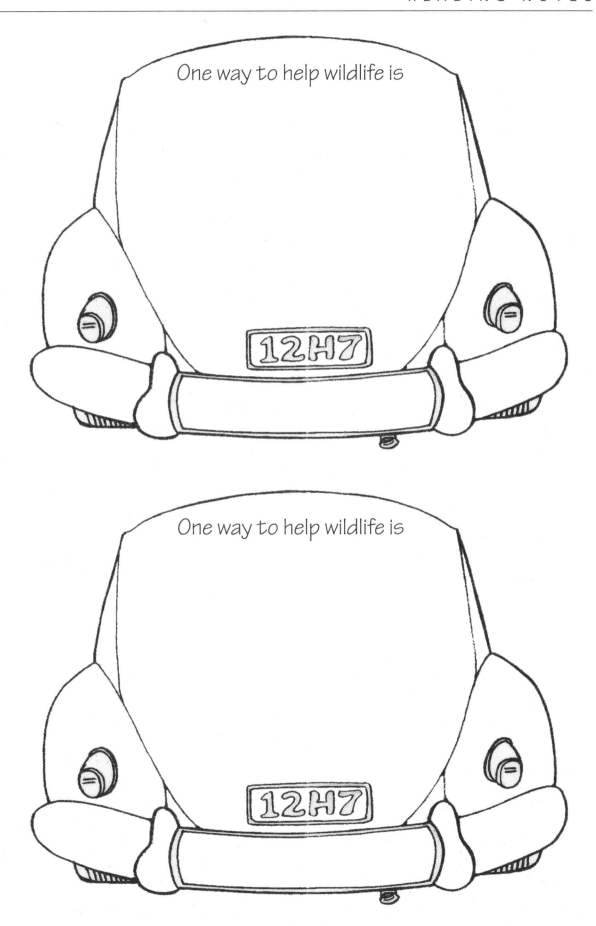

One way to help wildlife is

One way to help wildlife is

Read Sections 6-8 in the Student Text with your group.
Find three ideas for ways to help other people. For each
idea, complete the sentence on one of the cars. Then draw a
bumper sticker for that idea anywhere on the car.

One way to help other people is

12H7

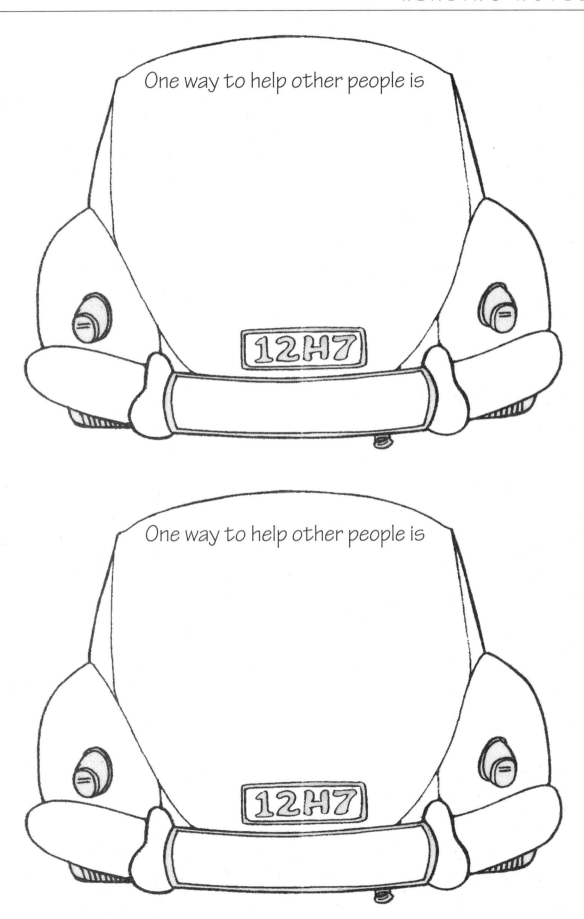

One way to help other people is

One way to help other people is

How Do Service Organizations Help Our Community?

Service organizations help in many ways. Some give medical help. Some build or repair houses for people in need. Some teach children and adults or work to make schools better. Some bring communities together by planning block parties, parades, picnics, and concerts.

Step 1: Use the library or the Internet to find out about a service organization that works in your community. Complete the chart below.

Name of organization
What it does
Who does the work
What problem is solved
Picture of its symbol or flag

Step 2: Use the information in your chart to write one or more paragraphs that answer the question: How does this service organization help our community?

In your writing, be sure to:

- introduce the topic and group related information together.
- develop the topic with facts, definitions, and details.
- use linking words and phrases to connect ideas.
- provide a concluding statement or section.

What does it mean to be a good citizen today? Draw a
picture, and write a caption.

Choose a hero from the reading. What did it mean to be a
good citizen during the hero's lifetime? Draw a picture, and
write a caption. Include the hero's name in the caption.

Compare good citizenship now and then. How is citizenship
similar? How is it different?

What are some problems in your community? Draw and describe three problems in your community below.

What is an *economy?* Make a collage of things that you think are related to our economy.

- Write ECONOMY large in the space below.
- Draw words and pictures around it.

Read Sections 1-4. For each section, write two things you learned about how our economy works.

1. We Buy and Sell Things	2. We Buy Goods and Services

United States Economy

3. The Things We Buy Are Scarce	4. There Are Benefits and Costs to What We Buy

Read Section 5, The Free Market Economy. Then complete the thought bubbles below.

I heard that we have a free market economy. What does that mean?

It means that…

How can you tell that the United States has a free market economy?

One piece of evidence is…

I wonder what other evidence we could find!

How Has Our Community's Economy Changed Over Time?

Step 1: Use the library or the Internet to learn how American Indians and the first white settlers in your community met their needs and wants long ago. Complete the charts.

American Indians Meet Their Needs and Wants

Food What did they gather, hunt, fish, or grow?	
Shelter and Clothing What did they make or build from nature?	
Trade What did they buy, sell, or barter?	

The First White Settlers Meet Their Needs and Wants

Food What did they gather, hunt, fish, or grow?	
Shelter and Clothing What did they make or build from nature?	
Trade How did they meet their needs and wants through trade?	

Step 2: Research how people in your community met their needs a century ago. Then compare to the present. How did the advantages and disadvantages of your community's location change over time?

People 100 Years Ago Meet Their Needs and Wants

Food	
Shelter and Clothing	
Transportation	
Communication	

We Meet Our Needs and Wants Today

Food	
Shelter and Clothing	
Transportation	
Communication	

1. Look at the timeline on this page.
    Fill in the blanks below. Use the words from the Word Bank.

    - The arrow on the left side of the timeline
      points to the _____.

    - The arrow on the right side of the timeline
      points to the _____.

    - From 1800 to 1899 is 100 years. This is called
      a _____.

    - The 1840s go from 1840 to 1849. This period of
      10 years is called a _____.

Word Bank

decade

future

past

century

A Timeline of Mail Service

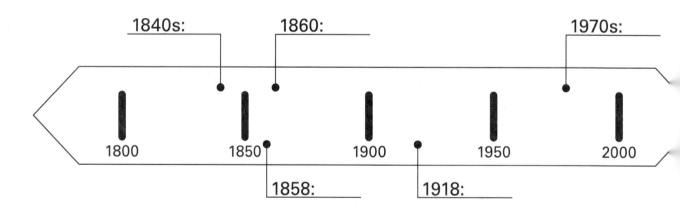

2. Here is a list of events. Write the letters of the events in the
   blanks next to the matching years on the timeline. Use the
   Student Text to help you.

   A. Pony Express starts.
   B. Companies offer
      overnight delivery.
   C. Mail is delivered by stagecoach.

   D. Airmail starts.
   E. Mail goes by ship around
      South America.

3. Choose one of the services on the timeline. In the space below,
   make an ad for the service. Draw a picture of the service. Write
   a slogan that tells customers why they should buy this service.

Read the two stories below.

Country A "My name is Marsha. The government in my country tells businesses what to make. It sets prices. There are only a few types of goods and services available. Sometimes I have to wait in a long line to buy food. The government tells us what types of jobs we can do."	**Country B** "My name is Kevin. In my country, I decide what type of job I want to do. Businesses choose who they want to hire and how much they want to pay their workers. When I go shopping, there are a wide variety of goods and services to choose from."

Does Country A or Country B have a free market economy? In the space below, create an argument.

- Write a claim that says which country you think has a free market economy.
- Explain two pieces of evidence that support your claim.
- Use linking words and phrases to connect opinion and reasons.

Complete the definitions below. Use your own words. Then draw and label the buyer and the seller in the picture of the fruit market.

A market is _____.

A buyer is _____.

A seller is _____.

Choices in a Free Market **127**

1. We Earn Money By Working

Why do people need to earn money?

Draw one way you can earn money.

List three ways adults can earn money.

1.

2.

3.

2. Businesses and the Economy

Examine this word diagram for "profit." Complete the diagram.

- Write a definition of "profit" in your own words.
- Draw a symbol of this word.
- Use this word in a sentence.
- Give an example from your life of this word.

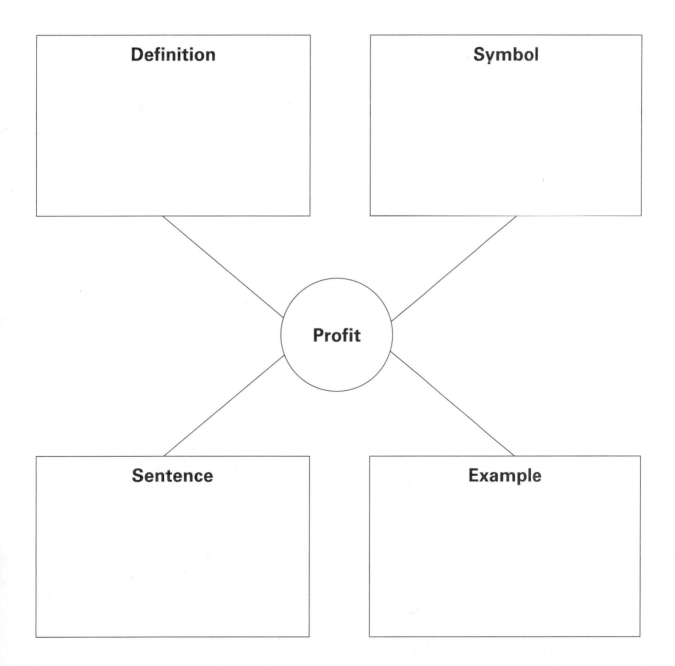

Definition

Symbol

Profit

Sentence

Example

3. Prices Change When Supply Is High and Demand Is Low

Follow the steps below to show what happens
when supply is high and demand is low.

1. Label the buyer and seller in the picture.

2. In the thought bubbles, write what each person is
   thinking when supply is high and demand is low.

3. Write a new price on the sign to show what
   happens when supply is high and demand is low.

4. Prices Change When Supply Is Low and Demand Is High

Follow the steps below to show what happens
when supply is low and demand is high.

1. Label the buyer and seller in the picture.

2. In the thought bubbles, write what each person is
   thinking when supply is low and demand is high.

3. Change the price on the sign to show what
   happens when supply is low and demand is high.

How Does Our Community Get The Resources We Need?

What resources do people in your community sell to or buy from other countries? Use the chart below to write what you learn.

Step 1: To find out what is sold, use the library or Internet, or ask adults.

Step 2: To find out what is bought, look at labels inside your clothing. Look on the back or bottom of dishes, shoes, and other things you use.

What We Sell	What We Buy	Countries We Trade With

You are one of your community's future resources. In fact, you are human capital. Human capital includes all the skills, talents, and knowledge that workers bring to their jobs.

Step 3: On the left side of the chart, list four or more skills that you are learning in school.

Step 4: Ask adult family members, friends, and neighbors how they use these skills in their work. Write their answers across from the correct skills in the chart.

What I Am Learning	How Others Use This at Work

Plan a presentation about an important entrepreneur.

- Use books and the Internet to research an important entrepreneur. As you research, list the primary and secondary sources you use to gather your information.

- Write a paragraph about why this entrepreneur is important in the space below. Use information from your research as evidence, and list your sources.

- Your presentation will need a prop or visual aid. Decide what you will use, and sketch it in the space below.

Explore the prices of fruits and vegetables where you live. In each box, draw or paste a picture of the item that matches the box's header. Write the item's price next to the word *Price*. Then answer the question next to the box. Be sure to use the words *supply* and *demand*.

High Supply and Low Demand = Low Price

Draw or paste a picture of the item here.

Why does this item have a low price?

_____

_____

_____

_____

_____

_____

_____

_____

Price: _____

Low Supply and High Demand = High Price

Draw or paste a picture of the item here.

Why does this item have a high price?

Price: _____

_____

_____

_____

_____

_____

_____

_____

_____

Suppose you are walking down the hallway of your school. You look down and see a $5 bill on the floor! What will you do?

- Brainstorm at least two options you have.

- Circle the option you would choose. Then explain why you would make this decision.

Situation 1: Birthday Money

It's your birthday! Your grandmother gives you a card. You look inside and see a $20 bill. What will you do with the money?

---

1. With your group, discuss each option. Circle the choice you would make.

   A. Use the money to buy something now.

   B. Save all the money for later.

   C. Spend $10 now. Save $10 for later.

   D. Give the money to someone in need.

2. In the space below, give two reasons that support your choice.

3. Read Section 1, People Save Money. List two reasons why people save money.

> **Situation 2: Saving Your Money**
> You have started saving the money you receive from gifts and from your allowance. But where should you put it?

1. With your group, discuss each option. Circle the choice you would make.

   A. Give the money to your teacher to keep it in the classroom.

   B. Hide the money at home.

   C. Put the money in a bank.

   D. Keep the money in a piggy bank in your room.

2. Give two reasons that support your choice.

3. Read Section 2, Ways People Save Money. List two reasons why it is good to keep your money in a bank.

> **Situation 3: Investing in Your Business**
> With the money you saved, you were able to start a business! On weekends, you make and sell lemonade in your neighborhood. What can you do to increase your profits?

1. With your group, discuss each option. Circle the choice you would make.

   A. Buy a machine that helps you make lemonade faster.

   B. Raise your prices extremely high.

   C. Shop around to find the cheapest lemons you can buy.

   D. Set aside profits to save up for an emergency.

2. Give two reasons that support your choice.

3. Read Sections 3 and 4. List two ways that businesses can use their money wisely.

What Economic Issues Are Important to Our Community?

Step 1: Ask questions. What questions do you have about these economic issues in your community? Record at least three in the left side of the chart below.

Step 2: Gather and evaluate sources. What are some possible answers to these questions? Do some research in the library or on the Internet and record what you find in the right side of the chart.

Economic Questions	Answers According to Research

Step 3: Take informed actions. What are people in your community doing to solve economic issues? Use the library or the Internet to research the answer to this question. Record your findings below.

What actions could you take to resolve economic issues in your community? List at least three below.

-

-

-

Review the budget Mr. Bessie's students used for their class party. Then answer the questions.

Item	Budget
Balloons	$10
Board Games	$30
Drinks and Snacks	$20
Music	$10
Money to Donate	$20
Money to Save	$10
Total	$100

1. How did the class decide on the budget?

2. Why was it important to add saving and donating to the budget?

3. Suppose that the budget is decreased to only $70. Do you think the students could still have the party? Explain which items you would reduce to meet the new budget.

Write an opinion piece that answers the Essential Question:
Why do we save money?

- Introduce the topic and state your opinion.
- Provide reasons that support your opinion.
- Use linking words and phrases *(because, therefore, since, for example)* to connect your opinion and reasons.
- Provide a concluding statement.

Cover and Title Page:
iStockphoto

Lesson 6

53: Raymond Gehman/Corbis
55: Wikimedia
58: dpa picture alliance/Alamy

Lesson 7

81T: iStockphoto
81C: Thinkstock
81B: Shutterstock

Lesson 8

85: Jim West/Alamy Stock Photo
86: Shutterstock
87: 2/Ocean/Corbis
88: Americanspirit/Dreamstime